101 WRITING PROMPTS
FOR MIDDLE SCHOOL

BOOKS FOR YOUNG WRITERS FROM RED WOLF PRESS:

Story Starters:
101 Story Starters for Little Kids by Maisy Day
101 Story Starters for Kids by Dena McMurdie
101 Story Starters for Teens by Maisy Day

Writing Prompts:
101 Writing Prompts for Middle School by Mark Trevor

101 WRITING PROMPTS

FOR MIDDLE SCHOOL

by
Mark Trevor

RED WOLF
PRESS

RED WOLF PRESS

This book was created to aid young writers learn and practice their writing skills in the classroom and at home. Red Wolf Press grants teachers the right to photocopy pages from this book for classroom use. No other part of this book may be reproduced in whole or in part or stored in a retrieval system. No part of this book may be transmitted in any form or by any means including electronic, mechanical, recording, photocopying, or any other means for commercial purposes or distribution without written consent from the publisher.

To contact the publisher about permissions, send an email to dmcmurdie@redwolfpress.com.

ISBN: 978-1-955731-03-4

Published by Red Wolf Press.

Interior design and cover design by Dena McMurdie.

Cover art by yusufdemirci, jannystockphoto, and MisterElements.

First printing, March 2023.

IMAGE CREDITS:

Front cover: all images depositphotos—background, hands, pencil, wood grain: yusufdemirci, doodles: MisterElements, post-it note: jannystockphoto.

Back cover: all images depositphotos—woodgrain, plant, pencil, post-it notes, paper clips: yusufdemirci, doodle: MisterElements.

Interior: All images depositphotos. **Page 5:** cat: 9george, **9:** books: Natasha_Pankina, **10-20:** speech bubbles, stars, heart: MisterElements, **21-30:** funny happy smiley faces: iliveinoctober, **31-40:** diverse faces of people: ArthurBalitskiy, **41-50:** Outdoor adventure doodles: stolenpencil, **61-70:** lightbulb: anfisa_focusova **71-80:** thumbs up: Ksania, **81-90:** sign post: Polina_Sova, **91-100:** brain: Ksania, **101-110:** award ribbon, trophy: lhfgraphicsz.

TABLE OF CONTENTS

FOR TEACHERS & PARENTS

Welcome! As a Language Arts teacher with over twenty years of classroom experience, I know how challenging it can be to engage students in writing assignments. That's why I created this book of fun writing prompts—to help students jump-start their imaginations and get words on the page.

This book contains over 100 exciting writing prompts for middle school students. I designed these prompts to help kids tap into their creativity and grow more comfortable sharing their thoughts. You'll find plenty of topics they enjoy writing about: themselves, friends, family, pets, and a few wild scenarios to keep things interesting.

These prompts are an excellent resource for teaching the standard writing categories—Narrative, Descriptive, Expository, and Persuasive. Most prompts work for multiple categories and a variety of exercises. Use them for assignments, warm-ups, journal entries, essays, creative writing, and more!

You don't need to follow a particular sequence or process with this book. However, Chapter 1: ALL ABOUT ME is a logical place to start, as students love to write about themselves.

I am honored that you chose my book, and I hope you find it the helpful resource I intended.

MARK TREVOR

FOR YOUNG WRITERS

Writing well and communicating your ideas is an essential skill, but it takes a lot of hard work to learn. Like anything else, practice will help you improve.

I have included a few tips below to help you become the best writer possible. Many will already be familiar to you.

1. Choose your words with care.

Using precise verbs and adjectives will make your writing more powerful and exciting.

Instead of:	Try:
ran	dashed, darted, sprinted
looked	glanced, stared, studied
threw	tossed, launched, flung, hurled
good, nice	fantastic, wonderful, excellent, superb
cold	freezing, glacial, wintry, icy, chilly
tired	exhausted, worn out

What other words can you think of? Use a thesaurus to find the best words to make your writing shine!

2. Check your mechanics

Punctuation, spelling, and capitalization—mistakes in these areas can distract your reader (or your teacher) and ruin an excellent piece of writing.

3. Don't forget the details.

Ideas need support, so make sure you include enough details and examples.

Instead of:	Try adding some details:
The dog was happy.	The dog perked up, and his tail swished back and forth.

Continues on the next page.

Instead of:	Try adding some details:
The girls became friends.	Anna and Jaycee spent every minute together. They painted each other's nails, read the same books, and had sleepovers every weekend.
Henry was nervous about the test.	Henry had dreaded this exam for weeks and spent last night tossing, turning, and waking up every few minutes.

4. Stay organized.

Your writing should flow well and be easy to understand. Use paragraphs to separate your ideas and keep things organized. An outline is like a plan of attack and can help you create a well-planned story or argument.

5. Edit. Edit. Edit.

Good writing takes hard work. Your first draft won't be perfect, and that's okay! It needs polishing and editing, and it will improve with each revision.

BONUS TIPS FOR ASPIRING AUTHORS

Do you love writing and want to develop your craft? I have two more tips for you:

1. Read. Read. Read!

The best writers spend plenty of time reading. Books, articles, news, webcomics—it doesn't matter what you read as long as you do plenty of it.

2. Practice. Practice. Practice!

It's the only way to improve. Here are some ways you can practice writing and have fun at the same time:

- Keep a journal
- Write song lyrics or poems
- Create a comic strip
- Write a novel

ALL ABOUT ME

Think of an interest or hobby you love. It could be sports, video games, drawing, or anything else. Describe your interest and how it began. What makes it so enjoyable?

_____

_____

_____

_____

_____

_____

_____

_____

_____

_____

_____

_____

_____

_____

_____

_____

_____

_____

_____

_____

_____

ALL ABOUT ME

Think about your favorite places to eat. Pick two and compare them. Consider their menu choices, atmosphere, and, of course, the food. Which one is your favorite?

_____

_____

_____

_____

_____

_____

_____

_____

_____

_____

_____

_____

_____

_____

_____

_____

_____

_____

ALL ABOUT ME

Think about your favorite season. What makes it your favorite?
Discuss the activities you enjoy during that time of year.

_____

_____

_____

_____

_____

_____

_____

_____

_____

_____

_____

_____

_____

_____

_____

_____

_____

_____

_____

ALL ABOUT ME

How would you describe yourself? Creative? Athletic? Kind? Stubborn? Pick a personality trait you have and share examples or experiences that show it in action.

_____

_____

_____

_____

_____

_____

_____

_____

_____

_____

_____

_____

_____

_____

_____

_____

_____

_____

_____

_____

ALL ABOUT ME

What is one thing you would like to change about yourself? Do you procrastinate? Are you impatient? Shy? Lazy? Identify something you wish to change. How could you improve in this area?

_____

_____

_____

_____

_____

_____

_____

_____

_____

_____

_____

_____

_____

_____

_____

_____

_____

_____

_____

_____

_____

ALL ABOUT ME

What are your pet peeves? Discuss two or three things that drive you crazy. How do you handle them?

_____

_____

_____

_____

_____

_____

_____

_____

_____

_____

_____

_____

_____

_____

_____

_____

_____

ALL ABOUT ME

Think of something in your past that you regret. Did you pass up a great opportunity? Perhaps a wonderful friendship fell apart. Describe what happened and what you learned from this experience.

_____

_____

_____

_____

_____

_____

_____

_____

_____

_____

_____

_____

_____

_____

_____

_____

_____

_____

_____

_____

_____

ALL ABOUT ME

What is your all-time favorite book or movie? Summarize the book or movie and tell why it's your favorite.

ALL ABOUT ME

What are your biggest fears? It could be heights, snakes, public speaking, or something else. Do you try to face this fear or avoid it? Explain how you deal with it.

_____

_____

_____

_____

_____

_____

_____

_____

_____

_____

_____

_____

_____

_____

_____

_____

_____

_____

_____

_____

ALL ABOUT ME

It's essential to have goals. What are your long-term goals? Do you want to attend college or start a business? Maybe you want to become rich, famous, or travel to exciting places. Give two or three goals and describe how you might achieve them.

_____

_____

_____

_____

_____

_____

_____

_____

_____

_____

_____

_____

_____

_____

_____

_____

_____

_____

_____

_____

_____

_____

ALL ABOUT ME

Who is someone you admire? What has this person done that inspires you?

_____
_____
_____
_____
_____
_____
_____
_____
_____
_____
_____
_____
_____
_____
_____
_____
_____
_____
_____
_____

OMG, SO AWKWARD!

When you enter Social Studies class, you feel a knot in your stomach. The substitute today is none other than... your mom!

What happens in class? Will your mom treat you like any other student or keep calling on you?

OMG, SO AWKWARD!

You get to class early—and stop in your tracks. Your best friend Rachel is leaning in to kiss your next-door neighbor, Landon. You see their lips touch! Ewww.

Do you pretend you didn't see them or ask Rachel a million questions after class? Does their kiss change your opinion of your best friend?

_____

_____

_____

_____

_____

_____

_____

_____

_____

_____

_____

_____

_____

_____

_____

_____

_____

_____

_____

_____

_____

OMG, SO AWKWARD!

You had a great field trip—sort of. You dash into the museum restroom, but when you come out, you find the place empty, and the school buses have left!

What do you do? Order an Uber? Call 911? How do you get back to school?

_____

_____

_____

_____

_____

_____

_____

_____

_____

_____

_____

_____

_____

_____

_____

_____

_____

_____

_____

_____

_____

OMG, SO AWKWARD!

You like walking your dog, Ranger, around the neighborhood and always pass Lucy's house. But when you stop to check your phone, Ranger squats to poop—right in Lucy's front yard. Oh no! Just then, Lucy and her mom pull up in their car.

What do you do next?

_____

_____

_____

_____

_____

_____

_____

_____

_____

_____

_____

_____

_____

_____

_____

_____

_____

_____

_____

_____

OMG, SO AWKWARD!

You're in math class doing homework when the secretary's voice comes over the classroom intercom: "Ms. Daniels, can you send Jackie Johnson to the office? Her mother is here with Jackie's eczema cream and her inhaler." Kids snicker, and your face turns twenty shades of red as you get up to leave.

What happens when you reach the office? Will you ever forgive your mom or the secretary?

_____

_____

_____

_____

_____

_____

_____

_____

_____

_____

_____

_____

_____

_____

_____

_____

_____

_____

_____

OMG, SO AWKWARD!

You love PE; it's your favorite class. But today, a soccer ball hits you square in the face. Dazed, you fall to the ground. When you open your eyes, your classmates (including your crush) are staring at you.

"Look at his lip! Ewww, he's bleeding. OMG, are those boogers coming out of his nose?"

Do you try to get up or lie there and pretend you're dead? What happens the rest of the day?

_____

_____

_____

_____

_____

_____

_____

_____

_____

_____

_____

_____

_____

_____

_____

_____

_____

_____

_____

_____

_____

OMG, SO AWKWARD!

You can't wait to find a seat in the crowded cafeteria and enjoy your lunch—pizza! Unfortunately, you don't notice the jello on the floor. You slip and fall on your butt, sending the entire tray into the air like exploding fireworks.

Where does your pizza end up? How do the other kids react? Do you get back in line? What happens next?

_____

_____

_____

_____

_____

_____

_____

_____

_____

_____

_____

_____

_____

_____

_____

_____

_____

_____

OMG, SO AWKWARD!

You munched on candy all morning, and by the end of math class, all those sour gummy treats churn in your stomach. When Ms. Connors asks you to approach the board, you rise from your seat, walk to the front, and puke out a rainbow of colors.

What do you do now? How do Ms. Connors and your grossed-out classmates react?

_____

_____

_____

_____

_____

_____

_____

_____

_____

_____

_____

_____

_____

_____

_____

_____

_____

_____

_____

_____

OMG, SO AWKWARD!

You fell asleep on the school bus again—no big deal. But when you get to school, kids stare at you and snicker. When you step into the restroom, you see it. Someone drew a goofy-looking mustache on you while you slept. You try your best, but the ink won't come off.

What do you do?

OMG, SO AWKWARD!

"What is that smell?" someone says as they pass you in the hallway. The odor is unidentifiable but horrible. More kids pass, each turning up their nose and giving you a dirty look. When you get home, you empty your backpack.

What happens next? Do you identify the mystery smell?

_____

_____

_____

_____

_____

_____

_____

_____

_____

_____

_____

_____

_____

_____

_____

_____

_____

_____

_____

_____

_____

_____

MY CRAZY FAMILY

Your parents/guardians have gone out of town for the entire week-end and left you home alone. You can do almost anything you wish. Describe everything you do on your fabulous weekend of freedom.

_____

_____

_____

_____

_____

_____

_____

_____

_____

_____

_____

_____

_____

_____

_____

_____

_____

_____

_____

_____

MY CRAZY FAMILY

Describe your family's pet (or one you want to have). Who takes care of it? What makes it interesting or fun to own? What do you like about it? Is there anything you don't like?

_____

_____

_____

_____

_____

_____

_____

_____

_____

_____

_____

_____

_____

_____

_____

_____

_____

_____

_____

MY CRAZY FAMILY

Your parents/guardians call you into the living room. They have a big announcement. Your mom is going to have a baby! What is your reaction? Shock? Joy? Confusion? How will this development affect you?

_____

_____

_____

_____

_____

_____

_____

_____

_____

_____

_____

_____

_____

_____

_____

_____

_____

_____

_____

_____

MY CRAZY FAMILY

You want a TV in your bedroom, but your parents/guardians don't think it's wise. What objections might they have? What can you say to convince them to let you get one?

_____

_____

_____

_____

_____

_____

_____

_____

_____

_____

_____

_____

_____

_____

_____

_____

_____

_____

_____

_____

MY CRAZY FAMILY

While playing with your friends, you scratch the car in the garage. When your parent/guardian asks you what happened, do you lie or tell the truth? What occurs as a result?

_____

_____

_____

_____

_____

_____

_____

_____

_____

_____

_____

_____

_____

_____

_____

_____

_____

_____

_____

MY CRAZY FAMILY

You must share a room with your brother or sister. Naturally, it would help if you established a few rules. What rules (give at least three) do you make so you can co-exist in relative harmony?

MY CRAZY FAMILY

Your cousin is visiting from out of state. You want to introduce them to your friends and show them your favorite places around town. Describe the activities you do together.

_____

_____

_____

_____

_____

_____

_____

_____

_____

_____

_____

_____

_____

_____

_____

_____

_____

_____

_____

MY CRAZY FAMILY

Describe your favorite family vacation. Where was it? What did you do there? What was the best part?

MY CRAZY FAMILY

Your sister wants highlights in her hair and asks you for help. You agree and get to work. An hour later, you remove the foil from her hair. Your sister screams. Her hair looks like a skunk is sitting on her head.

What do you do next?

_____

_____

_____

_____

_____

_____

_____

_____

_____

_____

_____

_____

_____

_____

_____

_____

_____

MY CRAZY FAMILY

Since you both love pizza, you and your parent/guardian decide to make one from scratch. (After some research and a trip to the store, you're ready.) What ingredients will you need? What steps (in sequence) do you follow to make a delicious pizza at home?

_____
_____
_____
_____
_____
_____
_____
_____
_____
_____
_____
_____
_____
_____
_____
_____
_____
_____
_____

AMAZING ADVENTURES

You are on an expedition to Antarctica to study the penguin population there. Describe the climate and what you notice about the penguins. What do you hope to learn on the trip?

AMAZING ADVENTURES

It's your first time on an airplane. Where is your destination? Describe your thoughts and sensations. Are you scared or excited? Do you look forward to flying again?

_____

_____

_____

_____

_____

_____

_____

_____

_____

_____

_____

_____

_____

_____

_____

_____

_____

_____

_____

_____

42

AMAZING ADVENTURES

You and your friend go hiking in the woods and get lost. It gets dark, and your cell phone battery dies. How do you find your way back?

_____

_____

_____

_____

_____

_____

_____

_____

_____

_____

_____

_____

_____

_____

_____

_____

_____

_____

_____

AMAZING ADVENTURES

On a humid summer night, the power goes out in your town. There is no TV, internet, air conditioning, etc. What do you and your family do for the next 24 hours?

_____
_____
_____
_____
_____
_____
_____
_____
_____
_____
_____
_____
_____
_____
_____
_____
_____
_____
_____
_____

AMAZING ADVENTURES

You join a team of marine biologists exploring the ocean depths in a special submarine.

Describe your experience in the vast underwater realm. What creatures do you see? What discoveries do you make?

_____

_____

_____

_____

_____

_____

_____

_____

_____

_____

_____

_____

_____

_____

_____

_____

_____

_____

_____

_____

AMAZING ADVENTURES

Out of nowhere, a devastating blizzard hits your town. As a result, you and your classmates get stuck at school for the weekend. What do you eat? How do you pass the time? How do you get home after the storm ends?

_____

_____

_____

_____

_____

_____

_____

_____

_____

_____

_____

_____

_____

_____

_____

_____

_____

_____

_____

_____

AMAZING ADVENTURES

Your guide leads you deep into the Amazon rainforest. It's brimming with beautiful and exotic plants and animals. Describe the sights and sounds that surround you. What is the purpose of your expedition, and what do you learn? What obstacles stand in your way?

_____

_____

_____

_____

_____

_____

_____

_____

_____

_____

_____

_____

_____

_____

_____

_____

_____

_____

AMAZING ADVENTURES

You are on a sailing adventure to the Galapagos Islands off the coast of South America. What do you think about as you sail toward your destination? What wildlife do you expect to see there?

_____

_____

_____

_____

_____

_____

_____

_____

_____

_____

_____

_____

_____

_____

_____

_____

_____

_____

_____

_____

_____

AMAZING ADVENTURES

You trek deep into the wilderness with a small group of hikers. As the temperatures fall, you make camp and start a fire. As darkness approaches, you hear frightening animal sounds. (Maybe Bigfoot is real!) Describe what happens that night.

_____

_____

_____

_____

_____

_____

_____

_____

_____

_____

_____

_____

_____

_____

_____

_____

_____

_____

_____

_____

AMAZING ADVENTURES

You get selected for the Olympic track team, and the coach chooses you to run in the relay race for the gold medal. Describe the event and your emotions as you and your team start and finish the race.

WOULD YOU RATHER?

Would you rather shrink to the size of a grasshopper or grow to the size of a T-Rex?

Explain your reasoning. Both sizes have pros and cons. Why did you pick that size? What challenges might await you?

_____

_____

_____

_____

_____

_____

_____

_____

_____

_____

_____

_____

_____

_____

_____

_____

_____

_____

_____

WOULD YOU RATHER?

Would you rather clean a dirty bathroom or a filthy kitchen?
Explain your choice. Describe what the job entails. Which job seems easier or more pleasant?

_____

_____

_____

_____

_____

_____

_____

_____

_____

_____

_____

_____

_____

_____

_____

_____

_____

_____

_____

WOULD YOU RATHER?

Would you rather spend a day crossing the desert or walking in the Arctic?

What made you pick that place? What gear, supplies, etc., would you need for that excursion?

_____

_____

_____

_____

_____

_____

_____

_____

_____

_____

_____

_____

_____

_____

_____

_____

_____

_____

_____

_____

WOULD YOU RATHER?

Would you rather be a vampire or a werewolf?
   Why did you pick that one? Describe an ordinary night as this creature.

_____

_____

_____

_____

_____

_____

_____

_____

_____

_____

_____

_____

_____

_____

_____

_____

_____

_____

_____

WOULD YOU RATHER?

Would you rather spend a day without food or a day without the internet?

Was this a tough choice? Why or why not? How do you spend your day?

_____

_____

_____

_____

_____

_____

_____

_____

_____

_____

_____

_____

_____

_____

_____

_____

_____

_____

WOULD YOU RATHER?

Would you rather time travel 100 years into the future or 100 years into the past?

Explain your choice. What is life like during that time?

_____

_____

_____

_____

_____

_____

_____

_____

_____

_____

_____

_____

_____

_____

_____

_____

_____

_____

_____

_____

_____

WOULD YOU RATHER?

Would you rather shave your head or shave off your eyebrows? Why did you pick that one? How do you explain this "new you" to others? How do you think people will react?

57

WOULD YOU RATHER?

Would you rather spend a year without television or a year without music?

Explain your choice. Which shows or artists would you miss the most?

_____

_____

_____

_____

_____

_____

_____

_____

_____

_____

_____

_____

_____

_____

_____

_____

_____

_____

_____

_____

WOULD YOU RATHER?

Would you rather live alone in a creepy old house or live with ten chimpanzees in a luxury hotel?

Why did you choose what you did? Describe your day-to-day life.

_____

_____

_____

_____

_____

_____

_____

_____

_____

_____

_____

_____

_____

_____

_____

_____

_____

_____

_____

_____

WOULD YOU RATHER?

Would you rather sleep with bed bugs for a week or eat only crickets for a week?

Which would be more difficult? Why?

_____

_____

_____

_____

_____

_____

_____

_____

_____

_____

_____

_____

_____

_____

_____

_____

_____

_____

_____

_____

WHAT WOULD YOU DO?

You often see kids at school get lunch and toss much of it away. Fresh fruit goes into the trash! So do unopened drinks and packages. Seeing so much food go to waste drives you crazy. What can prevent this? Where could you donate all this uneaten food?

_____

_____

_____

_____

_____

_____

_____

_____

_____

_____

_____

_____

_____

_____

_____

_____

_____

_____

_____

WHAT WOULD YOU DO?

You think school starts too early. The bus comes before dawn, and most students aren't awake until lunchtime. What time should school start? Give three convincing reasons for starting the school day at that time.

WHAT WOULD YOU DO?

You and your friends think teachers assign too much homework. You spend most of your free time on it, leaving little time for things you enjoy. How much homework should you get? Give three reasons why the amount of homework should be reduced.

_____

_____

_____

_____

_____

_____

_____

_____

_____

_____

_____

_____

_____

_____

_____

_____

_____

_____

_____

_____

WHAT WOULD YOU DO?

Kids want their cell phones in school, but teachers say the devices create problems. Come up with a solution that students and teachers might agree on. Think of three rules that allow students to have their phones in school without disrupting class or becoming a distraction. Explain the rules and consequences if they get broken.

WHAT WOULD YOU DO?

You want to buy something (e.g., a bike, a video game, sneakers, art supplies, etc.) but don't have the finances. How could you get the money? Will you do chores around the house or jobs for neighbors?

Describe what you want to buy, how much it costs, and how you plan to earn the money.

_____

_____

_____

_____

_____

_____

_____

_____

_____

_____

_____

_____

_____

_____

_____

_____

_____

_____

_____

_____

WHAT WOULD YOU DO?

You love football and want to try out for your middle school team, but your mom worries you will get hurt. Present a convincing argument you hope will change her mind and allow you to try out for the team.

WHAT WOULD YOU DO?

Should schools have dress codes, or should students be able to wear whatever they wish? Are pajamas and flip-flops okay? Can specific attire be distracting? Are some slogans or images offensive? Share your opinion and back it up with thoughtful examples or reasons.

WHAT WOULD YOU DO?

Should kids get allowances? If your answer is yes, explain. How much should they get, and how often should they receive it? Should they be required to complete chores or maintain good grades first? Support your opinion with specific details and reasons.

WHAT WOULD YOU DO?

You are pet-sitting your neighbor's dog, but it gets loose and runs down the street. How will you find and capture the runaway dog? Will you call the dog's owner or wait until you've caught it?

_____

_____

_____

_____

_____

_____

_____

_____

_____

_____

_____

_____

_____

_____

_____

_____

_____

_____

_____

WHAT WOULD YOU DO?

You get two invitations for the same day. One friend asks you to join them for a day trip to the beach. Another friend wants you to go to a sporting event. Both ideas sound great, but you have to pick one. How do you choose? What will you tell each friend?

_____

_____

_____

_____

_____

_____

_____

_____

_____

_____

_____

_____

_____

_____

_____

_____

_____

_____

_____

_____

IN MY OPINION

Cigarettes and vaping should be illegal. Do you agree or disagree?
Explain why.

_____

_____

_____

_____

_____

_____

_____

_____

_____

_____

_____

_____

_____

_____

_____

_____

_____

_____

_____

_____

_____

IN MY OPINION

Cats are better pets than dogs. Do you agree or disagree? Explain why.

IN MY OPINION

Middle and high schools should have vending machines so students can buy snacks and drinks. Do you agree or disagree? Explain why.

_____

_____

_____

_____

_____

_____

_____

_____

_____

_____

_____

_____

_____

_____

_____

_____

_____

_____

_____

_____

IN MY OPINION

There shouldn't be limits on "free speech." Do you agree or disagree? Explain why.

IN MY OPINION

You need a college education to become successful. Do you agree or disagree? Explain why.

_____

_____

_____

_____

_____

_____

_____

_____

_____

_____

_____

_____

_____

_____

_____

_____

_____

_____

_____

_____

_____

_____

IN MY OPINION

Theme parks (e.g., Disney World, Six Flags, etc.) are the best places to go on vacation. Do you agree or disagree? Explain why.

IN MY OPINION

Should theme parks like Sea World have performing whales, dolphins, and seals? Explain your opinion and discuss how animals in these parks should be treated.

_____

_____

_____

_____

_____

_____

_____

_____

_____

_____

_____

_____

_____

_____

_____

_____

_____

_____

_____

IN MY OPINION

Community service should be required to graduate from high school. Do you agree or disagree? Explain why.

_____

_____

_____

_____

_____

_____

_____

_____

_____

_____

_____

_____

_____

_____

_____

_____

_____

_____

_____

_____

_____

_____

IN MY OPINION

Your parents should never go through your phone. Do you agree or disagree? Explain why.

_____

_____

_____

_____

_____

_____

_____

_____

_____

_____

_____

_____

_____

_____

_____

_____

_____

_____

_____

_____

IN MY OPINION

Schools should eliminate letter and numerical grades, and all classes should be "pass" or "fail." Do you agree or disagree? Explain why.

_____

_____

_____

_____

_____

_____

_____

_____

_____

_____

_____

_____

_____

_____

_____

_____

_____

_____

_____

_____

_____

_____

CHOICES & CHALLENGES

Bullying is a big problem today. Has a bully targeted you or one of your friends? Describe what happened and how you/they responded. How should you handle bullies and bullying?

_____

_____

_____

_____

_____

_____

_____

_____

_____

_____

_____

_____

_____

_____

_____

_____

_____

_____

_____

_____

_____

CHOICES & CHALLENGES

What does the word "friendship" mean to you? Describe a person you know well (no name required) and how they exhibit the qualities of a true friend.

CHOICES & CHALLENGES

You have a crush on someone in your class. When you're hanging out with your best friend, you discover that you both like the same person. Write about your conversation and what you and your friend decide to do about this situation.

_____

_____

_____

_____

_____

_____

_____

_____

_____

_____

_____

_____

_____

_____

_____

_____

_____

_____

_____

_____

_____

CHOICES & CHALLENGES

Think of a time when something at school upset you. Write about what happened. Describe your emotions and how you reacted. What did you learn from this painful experience?

CHOICES & CHALLENGES

Your friend shares a secret and asks you not to tell anyone else. What do you do? When is it okay to keep a secret? When should you tell an adult? What type of secret is this?

CHOICES & CHALLENGES

You and your friends attend a party where a classmate offers you alcohol or marijuana. You know these substances are harmful and don't want to use them. What do you say? Do you leave or stay at the party? What happens when you see the classmate at school the next day?

CHOICES & CHALLENGES

A classmate texts you an inappropriate picture. Do you ignore it or text the person back and demand they stop? Do you tell someone about it? If so, who?

_____

_____

_____

_____

_____

_____

_____

_____

_____

_____

_____

_____

_____

_____

_____

_____

_____

_____

_____

_____

CHOICES & CHALLENGES

Before class begins, you see a classmate steal something from the teacher's desk. What do you do?

CHOICES & CHALLENGES

You and your best friend have an argument, so you're not speaking to one another. What do you do? Send a text or email? Call them? Or do you wait for them to contact you? How can you fix your relationship?

CHOICES & CHALLENGES

Somehow, a classmate has a copy of the answers for the final exam and offers them to you. How do you respond? Do you let the teacher know? If yes, do you reveal the classmate who has the test answers?

WHAT IF... ?

What if aliens start attending your school, and you become friends with one? One day, you go to your new friend's house. What are they like? What do you discover about your new friend and their family?

_____

_____

_____

_____

_____

_____

_____

_____

_____

_____

_____

_____

_____

_____

_____

_____

_____

_____

WHAT IF... ?

What if all your teachers got replaced by robots? Are the robots better or worse than the human teachers you had? What is the school like now? One student plans a revolt. What do you decide to do?

_____
_____
_____
_____
_____
_____
_____
_____
_____
_____
_____
_____
_____
_____
_____
_____
_____
_____
_____
_____
_____
_____

WHAT IF... ?

What if you could choose one superpower? What would you choose?
The ability to fly? To read minds? To become invisible? Describe
how you would use your unique ability.

_____

_____

_____

_____

_____

_____

_____

_____

_____

_____

_____

_____

_____

_____

_____

_____

_____

_____

_____

WHAT IF... ?

What if you could be your country's President or Prime Minister for a day? What do you do? What laws do you enact or eliminate?
   Before your day ends, you give a speech to the nation's citizens. What is your message to them?

_____

_____

_____

_____

_____

_____

_____

_____

_____

_____

_____

_____

_____

_____

_____

_____

_____

_____

_____

_____

WHAT IF... ?

What if you received a million dollars to spend however you wish? How do you use the money? What do you buy? Do you donate it or give any away? If so, to whom?

_____

_____

_____

_____

_____

_____

_____

_____

_____

_____

_____

_____

_____

_____

_____

_____

_____

_____

_____

_____

WHAT IF... ?

What if you could spend one day with anyone currently alive? It could be a parent, a famous athlete, a movie star, a musician, etc. Who do you choose? What do you do on that day?

_____

_____

_____

_____

_____

_____

_____

_____

_____

_____

_____

_____

_____

_____

_____

_____

_____

_____

_____

_____

_____

WHAT IF...?

What if you get taken captive aboard a pirate ship, where life is dreary and difficult? Describe the duties you must perform, the lousy food you have to eat, and the rowdy behavior of the pirates on board.

_____

_____

_____

_____

_____

_____

_____

_____

_____

_____

_____

_____

_____

_____

_____

_____

_____

_____

WHAT IF... ?

What if you and your family left Earth and moved to another planet? What is life like there? Describe your new home and your day-to-day activities.

_____

_____

_____

_____

_____

_____

_____

_____

_____

_____

_____

_____

_____

_____

_____

_____

_____

_____

_____

_____

_____

WHAT IF...?

What if a young black bear approaches you while you're walking in the woods? The bear's mother is nowhere in sight, and it looks friendly. You bring food and treats to the bear every day. What do you and the bear do during your daily encounters? Do you tell anyone about the bear?

_____

_____

_____

_____

_____

_____

_____

_____

_____

_____

_____

_____

_____

_____

_____

_____

_____

_____

_____

WHAT IF...?

What if you wake up in a medieval castle dressed like a knight? Moments later, a young prince or princess appears and says they need your help with a dragon destroying all the farmland. What is your plan to kill or expel the dragon? What happens when you confront the creature?

_____

_____

_____

_____

_____

_____

_____

_____

_____

_____

_____

_____

_____

_____

_____

_____

_____

_____

_____

_____

_____

_____

THE BEST & WORST THINGS

Sometimes siblings are wonderful, built-in friends. Other times, they are super annoying. Discuss the best and worst aspects of having siblings.

_____

_____

_____

_____

_____

_____

_____

_____

_____

_____

_____

_____

_____

_____

_____

_____

_____

_____

_____

_____

THE BEST & WORST THINGS

Teachers—the good, the bad, the ugly. Describe the best or worst teacher you ever had and what made them unforgettable.

THE BEST & WORST THINGS

Birthdays are usually good, and sometimes they are awesome. But now and then, they're horrible. Describe the best or worst birthday you've ever had.

THE BEST & WORST THINGS

The worst day of my life was_____. Why was it so terrible?
    As an alternative, write about the best day of your life. What happened? What made it so memorable?

_____
_____
_____
_____
_____
_____
_____
_____
_____
_____
_____
_____
_____
_____
_____
_____
_____
_____
_____
_____
_____
_____
_____
_____

THE BEST & WORST THINGS

Have you ever had a terrible experience on vacation? Describe what made it the worst vacation ever.

THE BEST & WORST THINGS

Pets are wonderful but also a lot of work. What are the best and worst aspects of having a pet?

THE BEST & WORST THINGS

What is the best age? Sixteen years old? Eighteen? Twenty-one?
Choose an age and explain why you picked it.

THE BEST & WORST THINGS

What is the best type of music? Rock? Hip Hop? Country? Classical? Explain why that music is your favorite—and better than other forms.

_____

_____

_____

_____

_____

_____

_____

_____

_____

_____

_____

_____

_____

_____

_____

_____

_____

_____

_____

_____

THE BEST & WORST THINGS

Where is the best place to live? The city, the country, the suburbs, or somewhere else? Explain why you prefer to live in that area.

_____

_____

_____

_____

_____

_____

_____

_____

_____

_____

_____

_____

_____

_____

_____

_____

_____

_____

_____

_____

THE BEST & WORST THINGS

What foods do you think are the absolute best? Bacon? Sushi? Pizza? Would your friends agree with you? Rank your top three favorite foods and explain why they are the best.

ABOUT THE AUTHOR

MARK TREVOR has been a language arts teacher for nearly 25 years and has taught students from kindergarten through grade 12. He currently lives in Cary, North Carolina.

Made in the USA
Las Vegas, NV
11 January 2024

84210539R00063